C000052538

FOLENS MATHS WEEKLY ASSESSMENT

Book 3

Hilary Koll

Steve Mills

Folens Publishers

Introduction

Weekly Assessment and the National Numeracy Framework

Each of the six books in this series provides 34 sharply focused assessments that address the Year's National Numeracy Framework learning objectives. They are arranged in accordance with the five divisions of each yearly teaching programme, and will help teachers to review and record the progress children are making in relation to the learning objectives during each year of school.

The assessments

Assessments consist of either written questions or a mix of written and orally delivered questions, depending on the nature of the objectives. In both cases, the format ensures quick and easy marking.

Assessment administration

Each assessment will take approximately 20–30 minutes of class time, and might follow or conclude the final Mathematics session of the week. Assessments should be selected according to what has been taught in the week. Where an assessment includes oral questions it is recommended that these are delivered at the start and that no more than 5 seconds are given for each question.

Each assessment consists of two pages – a teacher page and a pupil page.

The teacher page includes:

- a list of the learning objectives in a division of the yearly teaching programme to provide overall context, together with the specific objectives assessed in the test (highlighted in bold type) and the related question numbers

- teacher notes that point out typical misconceptions and errors and also offer teaching tips

- oral questions for those tests that include oral work

- answers.

The pupil page is a page with questions and space for answers.

In addition, there is a photocopiable record sheet provided to allow you to record weekly assessment marks for all pupils.

Acknowledgements

Folens allows photocopying of pages marked 'copiable page' for educational use, providing that this use is within the confines of the purchasing institution. Copiable pages should not be declared in any return in respect of any photocopying licence.

Folens books are protected by international copyright laws. All rights are reserved. The copyright of all materials in this book, except where otherwise stated, remains the property of the publisher and authors. No part of this publication may be reproduced, stored in a retrieval system, or transmitted, in any form or by any means, for whatever purpose, without the written permission of Folens Limited.

Hilary Koll and Steve Mills hereby assert their moral rights to be identified as the authors of this work in accordance with the Copyright, Designs and Patents Act 1988.

Editor: Hayley Willer   Layout artist: Philippa Jarvis
Cover design: Ed Gallagher   Illustrations: Susan Hutchison
Cover photograph: Kelvin Freeman (With thanks to Grove Park Primary School, Chiswick.)

© 1999 Folens Limited, on behalf of the authors.

Summary of teaching programme objectives from the *Framework for Teaching Mathematics*, published by the DfEE as part of the National Numeracy Strategy.

First published 1999 by Folens Limited, Dunstable and Dublin.

Folens Limited, Albert House, Apex Business Centre, Boscombe Road, Dunstable, LU5 4RL, United Kingdom. Reprinted 2000.

ISBN 186202 824–9

Printed in Singapore by Craft Print.

Contents

Activity sheet questions

Oral
1–10
- Describe and extend number sequences:
  - count on or back in tens or hundreds, starting from any two- or three-digit number

Written
1–2 – count on or back in twos starting from any two-digit number
3–5 – count on in steps of 3, 4 or 5 from any small number to at least 50, then back again
  - recognise odd and even numbers to at least 100.
- Recognise two-digit and three-digit multiples of 2, 5 or 10, and three-digit multiples of 50 and 100.

Teacher note

- Number lines and counting sticks can be used to help children to count on and back.

Oral questions

1. Count on 8 from 87.
2. Count on 12 from 123.
3. Count on 30 in tens from 50.
4. Count on 50 in tens from 167.
5. Count on 400 in hundreds from 236.
6. Count back 7 from 59.
7. Count back 8 from 43.
8. Count back 40 in tens from 53.
9. Count back 300 in hundreds from 456.
10. Count back 600 in hundreds from 912.

Answers

1. **95**	6. **52**
2. **135**	7. **35**
3. **80**	8. **13**
4. **217**	9. **156**
5. **636**	10. **312**

1 Write the next five numbers. 10, 12, 14 … | **16, 18, 20, 22, 24**

2 Write the next five numbers. 32, 30, 28 … | **26, 24, 22, 20, 18**

3 a. Continue the pattern in the path.

15   18   21   **24   27**   30   33   36

b. Explain the rule. | **Goes up in threes.**

4 a. Fill in the missing numbers in the caterpillar.

22   26   30   **34   38   42   46   50   54**

b. Explain the rule. | **Goes up in fours.**

5 Fill in the missing numbers in the scarf.

45   50   **55   60   65   70   75   80**   85

Name: _____   Date: _____

1.	6.
2.	7.
3.	8.
4.	9.
5.	10.

1 Write the next five numbers. 10, 12, 14 …

2 Write the next five numbers. 32, 30, 28 …

3 a. Continue the pattern in the path.

15   18   21

b. Explain the rule.

4 a. Fill in the missing numbers in the caterpillar.

22   26   30

b. Explain the rule.

5 Fill in the missing numbers in the scarf.

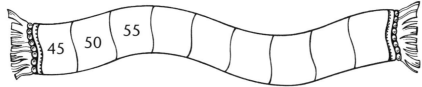

45   50   55

Activity sheet questions

- Describe and extend number sequences:
  - count on or back in tens or hundreds, starting from any two- or three-digit number
  - count on or back in twos starting from any two-digit number
  - count on in steps of 3, 4 or 5 from any small number to at least 50, then back again

Written
1–2
3–7
- recognise odd and even numbers to at least 100.
- Recognise two-digit and three-digit multiples of 2, 5 or 10, and three-digit multiples of 50 and 100.

Teacher note

- Children need to understand that it is the units digit that determines whether a number is odd or even, however large the number.

Answers

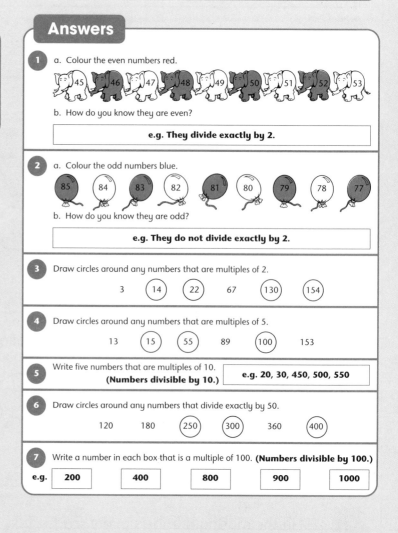

1 a. Colour the even numbers red.

45 46 47 48 49 50 51 52 53

b. How do you know they are even?

e.g. They divide exactly by 2.

2 a. Colour the odd numbers blue.

85 84 83 82 81 80 79 78 77

b. How do you know they are odd?

e.g. They do not divide exactly by 2.

3 Draw circles around any numbers that are multiples of 2.

3 (14) (22) 67 (130) (154)

4 Draw circles around any numbers that are multiples of 5.

13 (15) (55) 89 (100) 153

5 Write five numbers that are multiples of 10.
(Numbers divisible by 10.) **e.g. 20, 30, 450, 500, 550**

6 Draw circles around any numbers that divide exactly by 50.

120 180 (250) (300) 360 (400)

7 Write a number in each box that is a multiple of 100. **(Numbers divisible by 100.)**

e.g. 200 400 800 900 1000

Name: _____   Date: _____

1 a. Colour the even numbers red.

45 46 47 48 49 50 51 52 53

b. How do you know they are even?

| |
| |

2 a. Colour the odd numbers blue.

85 84 83 82 81 80 79 78 77

b. How do you know they are odd?

| |
| |

3 Draw circles around any numbers that are multiples of 2.

3   14   22   67   130   154

4 Draw circles around any numbers that are multiples of 5.

13   15   55   89   100   153

5 Write five numbers that are multiples of 10.

6 Draw circles around any numbers that divide exactly by 50.

120   180   250   300   360   400

7 Write a number in each box that is a multiple of 100.

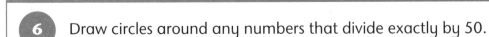

Activity sheet questions

Written

1–3

● **Read and write whole numbers to at least 1000 in figures and words.**

● Know what each digit represents, and partition three-digit numbers into a multiple of 100, a multiple of ten and ones (HTU).

● Read and begin to write the vocabulary of comparing and ordering numbers, including ordinal numbers to at least 100.
Compare two given three-digit numbers, say which is more or less, and give a number which lies between them.

● Say the number that is 1, 10 or 100 more or less than any given two- or three-digit number.

● Order whole numbers to at least 1000, and position them on a number line.

Teacher note

● Emphasise that each column is worth ten times more than the column to its right. Columns to the left become larger in value and columns to the right become smaller in value. Practical materials, such as base 10 apparatus can assist to model this and help children to see the relationships.

Answers

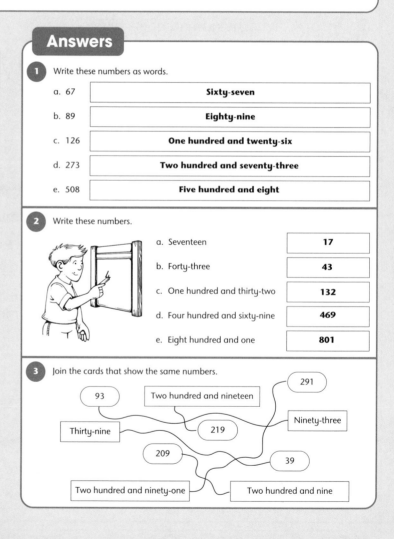

1 Write these numbers as words.

a. 67 — **Sixty-seven**

b. 89 — **Eighty-nine**

c. 126 — **One hundred and twenty-six**

d. 273 — **Two hundred and seventy-three**

e. 508 — **Five hundred and eight**

2 Write these numbers.

a. Seventeen — **17**

b. Forty-three — **43**

c. One hundred and thirty-two — **132**

d. Four hundred and sixty-nine — **469**

e. Eight hundred and one — **801**

3 Join the cards that show the same numbers.

93 Two hundred and nineteen 291

Thirty-nine 219 Ninety-three

209 39

Two hundred and ninety-one Two hundred and nine

Name: _____   Date: _____

1 Write these numbers as words.

a. 67

b. 89

c. 126

d. 273

e. 508

2 Write these numbers.

a. Seventeen

b. Forty-three

c. One hundred and thirty-two

d. Four hundred and sixty-nine

e. Eight hundred and one

3 Join the cards that show the same numbers.

291

93   Two hundred and nineteen

Ninety-three

Thirty-nine   219

209

39

Two hundred and ninety-one   Two hundred and nine

Place value and ordering

Activity sheet questions

Written
1–6
7–8

- Read and write whole numbers to at least 1000 in figures and words.
- **Know what each digit represents.**
  Partition three-digit numbers into a multiple of 100, a multiple of ten and ones (HTU).
- Read and begin to write the vocabulary of comparing and ordering numbers, including ordinal numbers to at least 100.
  Compare two given three-digit numbers, say which is more or less, and give a number which lies between them.
- Say the number that is 1, 10 or 100 more or less than any given two- or three-digit number.
- Order whole numbers to at least 1000, and position them on a number line.

Teacher note

- When partitioning numbers into hundreds, tens and units children can be confused by the use of zero as a 'place holder' as in 305, 280, etc. In our place-value system zero is used simply to indicate the presence of a column, even though it is empty, thus we read 603 rather than 63.

Answers

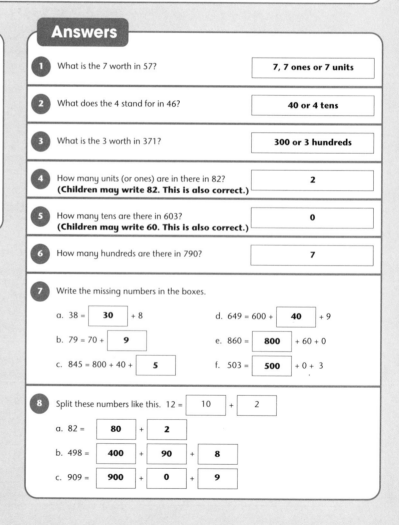

1. What is the 7 worth in 57? — **7, 7 ones or 7 units**

2. What does the 4 stand for in 46? — **40 or 4 tens**

3. What is the 3 worth in 371? — **300 or 3 hundreds**

4. How many units (or ones) are in there in 82?
   (Children may write 82. This is also correct.) — **2**

5. How many tens are there in 603?
   (Children may write 60. This is also correct.) — **0**

6. How many hundreds are there in 790? — **7**

7. Write the missing numbers in the boxes.

   a. 38 = **30** + 8   d. 649 = 600 + **40** + 9

   b. 79 = 70 + **9**   e. 860 = **800** + 60 + 0

   c. 845 = 800 + 40 + **5**   f. 503 = **500** + 0 + 3

8. Split these numbers like this. 12 = 10 + 2

   a. 82 = **80** + **2**

   b. 498 = **400** + **90** + **8**

   c. 909 = **900** + **0** + **9**

Name: _____   Date: _____

1   What is the 7 worth in 57?

2   What does the 4 stand for in 46?

3   What is the 3 worth in 371?

4   How many units (or ones) are in there in 82?

5   How many tens are there in 603?

6   How many hundreds are there in 790?

7   Write the missing numbers in the boxes.

a.   38 = [   ] + 8   d.   649 = 600 + [   ] + 9

b.   79 = 70 + [   ]   e.   860 = [   ] + 60 + 0

c.   845 = 800 + 40 + [   ]   f.   503 = [   ] + 0 + 3

8   Split these numbers like this.   12 = [10] + [2]

a.   82 = [   ] + [   ]

b.   498 = [   ] + [   ] + [   ]

c.   909 = [   ] + [   ] + [   ]

Place value and ordering

Activity sheet questions

Written 1–9

- Read and write whole numbers to at least 1000 in figures and words.
- Know what each digit represents, and partition three-digit numbers into a multiple of 100, a multiple of ten and ones (HTU).
- **Read and begin to write the vocabulary of comparing and ordering numbers, including ordinal numbers to at least 100.**
  Compare two given three-digit numbers, say which is more or less, and give a number which lies between them.
- Say the number that is 1, 10 or 100 more or less than any given two- or three-digit number.
- Order whole numbers to at least 1000, and position them on a number line.

Teacher note

- The use of number lines is essential for comparing and ordering. Counting sticks can be used for further illustration.
- Remind the children to read the sequence of patterns from left to right in questions 1 and 2.

Answers

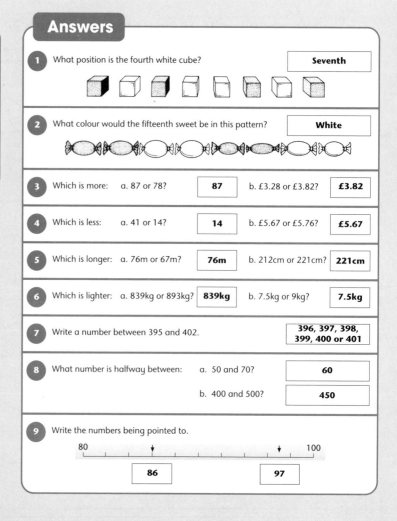

1 What position is the fourth white cube? **Seventh**

2 What colour would the fifteenth sweet be in this pattern? **White**

3 Which is more: a. 87 or 78? **87** b. £3.28 or £3.82? **£3.82**

4 Which is less: a. 41 or 14? **14** b. £5.67 or £5.76? **£5.67**

5 Which is longer: a. 76m or 67m? **76m** b. 212cm or 221cm? **221cm**

6 Which is lighter: a. 839kg or 893kg? **839kg** b. 7.5kg or 9kg? **7.5kg**

7 Write a number between 395 and 402. **396, 397, 398, 399, 400 or 401**

8 What number is halfway between: a. 50 and 70? **60**

   b. 400 and 500? **450**

9 Write the numbers being pointed to.

80 — 86 — 97 — 100

86 **97**

Name: _____ Date: _____

Place value and ordering

1 What position is the fourth white cube?

2 What colour would the fifteenth sweet be in this pattern?

3 Which is more: a. 87 or 78?   b. £3.28 or £3.82?

4 Which is less: a. 41 or 14?   b. £5.67 or £5.76?

5 Which is longer: a. 76m or 67m?   b. 212cm or 221cm?

6 Which is lighter: a. 839kg or 893kg?   b. 7.5kg or 9kg?

7 Write a number between 395 and 402.

8 What number is halfway between: a. 50 and 70?

b. 400 and 500?

9 Write the numbers being pointed to.

80   100

Activity sheet questions

- Read and write whole numbers to at least 1000 in figures and words.
- Know what each digit represents and partition three-digit numbers into a multiple of 100, a multiple of ten and ones (HTU).
- Read and begin to write the vocabulary of comparing and ordering numbers, including ordinal numbers to at least 100.
  Compare two given three-digit numbers, say which is more or less, and give a number which lies between them.

Oral
1–10
& Written
  1–3
- Say the number that is 1, 10 or 100 more or less than any given two- or three-digit number.
  4–6
- Order whole numbers to at least 1000, and position them on a number line.

Teacher note

- The use of place-value cards is useful for demonstrating that when adding or subtracting 100, for example, the tens and units digits remain unchanged. When adding or subtracting 10 the units digit remains unchanged.

Oral questions

What number is 1 more than:
1. 59?
2. 164?
3. 399?

What number is 1 less than:
4. 87?
5. 260?

What number is 10 more than:
6. 83?
7. 197?
8. 590?

What number is 10 less than:
9. 239?
10. 602?

Answers

1.	**60**	6.	**93**
2.	**165**	7.	**207**
3.	**400**	8.	**600**
4.	**86**	9.	**229**
5.	**259**	10.	**592**

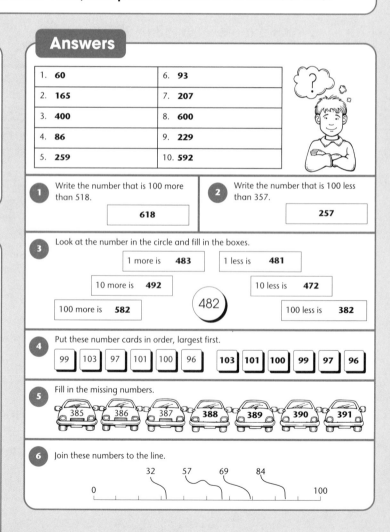

1 Write the number that is 100 more than 518.
618

2 Write the number that is 100 less than 357.
257

3 Look at the number in the circle and fill in the boxes.

1 more is **483** 1 less is **481**
10 more is **492** 10 less is **472**
(482)
100 more is **582** 100 less is **382**

4 Put these number cards in order, largest first.
99 103 97 101 100 96
103 **101** **100** **99** **97** **96**

5 Fill in the missing numbers.
385 386 387 388 389 390 391

6 Join these numbers to the line.
32 57 69 84
0   100

Name: _____ Date: _____

Place value and ordering

ASSESSMENT 6

1.	6.
2.	7.
3.	8.
4.	9.
5.	10.

1 Write the number that is 100 more than 518.

2 Write the number that is 100 less than 357.

3 Look at the number in the circle and fill in the boxes.

1 more is

1 less is

10 more is

10 less is

100 more is

482

100 less is

4 Put these number cards in order, largest first.

| 99 | 103 | 97 | 101 | 100 | 96 |

5 Fill in the missing numbers.

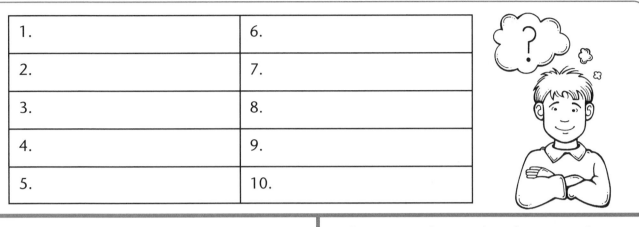

385 386 387

6 Join these numbers to the line.

32   57   69   84

0   100

Activity sheet questions

Written

1–2 • Read and begin to write the vocabulary of estimation and approximation.
Give a sensible estimate of up to about 100 objects.

3–6 • Round any two-digit number to the nearest 10 and any three-digit number to
the nearest 100.

Teacher note

• Many children will initially need the support of number lines marked from 0 to 100 in tens and from 0 to 1000 in hundreds to help them to round correctly.

Answers

1 a. Write the numbers you think are being pointed to.

0 ↓ ↓ 10

(Answers close to these values are acceptable.) [3] [8]

b. How did you decide? [**e.g. I split the line into 10 pieces.**]

2 a. Write the numbers you think are being pointed to.

0 ↓ ↓ 100

[20] [60] **(Answers close to these values are acceptable.)**

b. How did you decide? [**e.g. I split the line into 10 pieces.**]

3 Round these numbers to the nearest 10.

a. 46 [**50**] b. 64 [**60**] c. 85 [**90**]

4 Write a number between 50 and 60 that is nearer to 50.
(Any number between 51 and 54 inclusive.) [**e.g. 52**]

5 Round these measurements to the nearest 10 units.

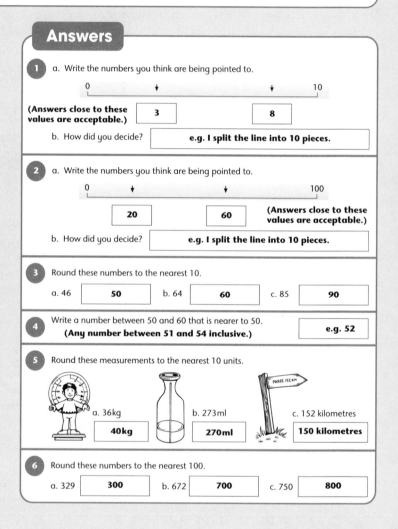

a. 36kg [**40kg**] b. 273ml [**270ml**] c. 152 kilometres [**150 kilometres**]

6 Round these numbers to the nearest 100.

a. 329 [**300**] b. 672 [**700**] c. 750 [**800**]

Name: _____ Date: _____

Estimating and rounding

1 a. Write the numbers you think are being pointed to.

0 ↓ ↓ 10

[ ]   [ ]

b. How did you decide? [   ]

2 a. Write the numbers you think are being pointed to.

0 ↓ ↓ 100

[ ]   [ ]

b. How did you decide? [   ]

3 Round these numbers to the nearest 10.

a. 46 [   ]   b. 64 [   ]   c. 85 [   ]

4 Write a number between 50 and 60 that is nearer to 50. [   ]

5 Round these measurements to the nearest 10 units.

a. 36 kg   b. 273 ml   c. 152 kilometres

PARIS 152 KM

[   ]   [   ]   [   ]

6 Round these numbers to the nearest 100.

a. 329 [   ]   b. 672 [   ]   c. 750 [   ]

Fractions

Activity sheet questions

Written

1–7

- Recognise unit fractions such as $\frac{1}{2}$, $\frac{1}{3}$, $\frac{1}{4}$, $\frac{1}{5}$, $\frac{1}{10}$ … and use them to find fractions of shapes and numbers.

  Begin to recognise simple fractions that are several parts of a whole, such as $\frac{3}{4}$, $\frac{2}{3}$ or $\frac{3}{10}$.

  Begin to recognise simple equivalent fractions: for example, five tenths and one half, five fifths and one whole.

  Compare familiar fractions: for example, know that on the number line one half lies between one quarter and three quarters.

  Estimate a simple fraction.

Teacher note

- Children often have more difficulty when expressing a fraction of a set than of an area. The idea that 3 coloured balls in a bag of 4, for example, represent a number less than 1 can take some time to assimilate.

Answers

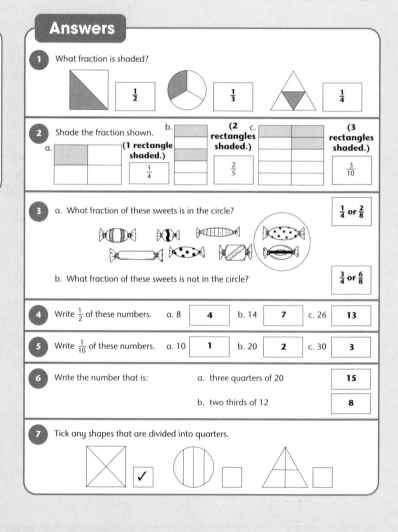

Name: _____   Date: _____

1 What fraction is shaded?

    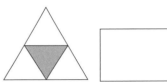

2 Shade the fraction shown.

a.  $\frac{1}{4}$

b. 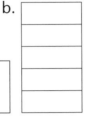 $\frac{2}{5}$

c.  $\frac{3}{10}$

3 a. What fraction of these sweets is in the circle?

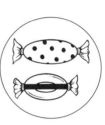

b. What fraction of these sweets is not in the circle?

4 Write $\frac{1}{2}$ of these numbers.   a. 8 [   ]   b. 14 [   ]   c. 26 [   ]

5 Write $\frac{1}{10}$ of these numbers.   a. 10 [   ]   b. 20 [   ]   c. 30 [   ]

6 Write the number that is: a. three quarters of 20 [   ]

b. two thirds of 12 [   ]

7 Tick any shapes that are divided into quarters.

    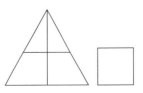

Fractions

Activity sheet questions

- Recognise unit fractions such as $\frac{1}{2}$, $\frac{1}{3}$, $\frac{1}{4}$, $\frac{1}{5}$, $\frac{1}{10}$ ... and use them to find fractions of shapes and numbers.

  Begin to recognise simple fractions that are several parts of a whole, such as $\frac{3}{4}$, $\frac{2}{3}$ or $\frac{3}{10}$.

Written

1–2 **Begin to recognise simple equivalent fractions: for example, five tenths and one half, five fifths and one whole.**

3–4 **Compare familiar fractions: for example, know that on the number line one half lies between one quarter and three quarters.**

5–6 **Estimate a simple fraction.**

Teacher note

- Children often need much experience of fractions as areas and subsets before they can meaningfully mark fractions on a number line.

Answers

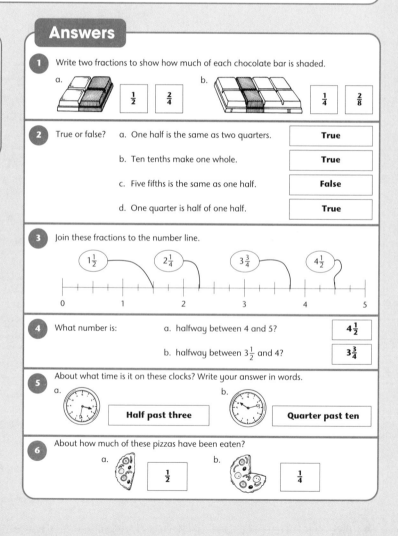

1 Write two fractions to show how much of each chocolate bar is shaded.

a. $\frac{1}{2}$ $\frac{2}{4}$

b. $\frac{1}{4}$ $\frac{2}{8}$

2 True or false?

a. One half is the same as two quarters. **True**

b. Ten tenths make one whole. **True**

c. Five fifths is the same as one half. **False**

d. One quarter is half of one half. **True**

3 Join these fractions to the number line.

$1\frac{1}{2}$ $2\frac{1}{4}$ $3\frac{3}{4}$ $4\frac{1}{2}$

0 1 2 3 4 5

4 What number is:

a. halfway between 4 and 5? $4\frac{1}{2}$

b. halfway between $3\frac{1}{2}$ and 4? $3\frac{3}{4}$

5 About what time is it on these clocks? Write your answer in words.

a. **Half past three**

b. **Quarter past ten**

6 About how much of these pizzas have been eaten?

a. $\frac{1}{2}$

b. $\frac{1}{4}$

Name: _____   Date: _____

1 Write two fractions to show how much of each chocolate bar is shaded.

a.  ☐ ☐

b. 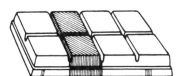 ☐ ☐

2 True or false?

a. One half is the same as two quarters. ☐

b. Ten tenths make one whole. ☐

c. Five fifths is the same as one half. ☐

d. One quarter is half of one half. ☐

3 Join these fractions to the number line.

$1\frac{1}{2}$ $2\frac{1}{4}$ $3\frac{3}{4}$ $4\frac{1}{2}$

0   1   2   3   4   5

4 What number is:

a. halfway between 4 and 5? ☐

b. halfway between $3\frac{1}{2}$ and 4? ☐

5 About what time is it on these clocks? Write your answer in words.

a.

b.

6 About how much of these pizzas have been eaten?

a. ☐

b. ☐

Activity sheet questions

Oral
1–10
Written
1–5

- Use known number facts and place value to add/subtract mentally.

- Use knowledge that addition can be done in any order to do mental calculations more efficiently. For example:
  - put the larger number first and count on
  - add three or four small numbers by putting the largest number first and/or by finding pairs totalling 9, 10 or 11
    - partition into '5 and a bit' when adding 6, 7, 8 or 9 (e.g. 47 + 8 = 45 + 2 + 5 + 3 = 50 + 5 = 55)
    - partition into tens and units, then recombine (e.g. 34 + 53 = 30 + 50 + 4 + 3).
- Find a small difference by counting up from the smaller to the larger number (e.g. 102 – 97).
- Identify near doubles, using doubles already known (e.g. 80 + 81).
- Add and subtract mentally a 'near multiple of 10' to or from a two-digit number … by adding or subtracting 10, 20, 30 … and adjusting.
- Use patterns of similar calculations.
- Say or write a subtraction statement corresponding to a given addition statement, and vice versa.
- Bridge through a multiple of 10, then adjust.

Teacher note

- Help children to develop a range of strategies, e.g. when adding 11, add 10 and add a further 1, etc. Remind children that the order does not matter when adding.

Oral questions

1. What is 6 more than 153?
2. How many more is 348 than 5?
3. 100 plus 53.
4. 300 add 27.
5. What is the difference between 200 and 6?
6. 800 subtract 8.
7. 70 plus 38.
8. 40 add 57.
9. 56 take 32.
10. How much fewer is 55 than 78?

Answers

1.	159	6.	792
2.	343	7.	108
3.	153	8.	97
4.	327	9.	24
5.	194	10.	23

1. Write the answers in the boxes.

a. 5 + 72 = **77**   b. 4 + 135 = **139**   c. 9 + 146 = **155**

2 a. 30 + 50 = **80**   b. 20 + 47 = **67**   c. 40 + 59 = **99**

3 a. 8 + 6 + 3 + 7 = **24**   b. 4 + 8 + 7 + 2 = **21**

4 a. 12 + 6 + 8 + 7 **33**   b. 16 + 9 + 3 + 4 **32**

5 Write the missing numbers in the boxes.

a. 8 + **7** + 6 = 21   b. **18** + 7 + 9 = 34

10 Mental calculation strategies (+ and –)

1.	6.
2.	7.
3.	8.
4.	9.
5.	10.

1 Write the answers in the boxes.

a. 5 + 72 = [ ]   b. 4 + 135 = [ ]   c. 9 + 146 = [ ]

2 a. 30 + 50 = [ ]   b. 20 + 47= [ ]   c. 40 + 59 = [ ]

3 a. 8 + 6 + 3 + 7 = [ ]   b. 4 + 8 + 7 + 2 = [ ]

4 a. 12 + 6 + 8 + 7 [ ]   b. 16 + 9 + 3 + 4 [ ]

5 Write the missing numbers in the boxes.

a. 8 + [ ] + 6 = 21   b. [ ] + 7 + 9 = 34

Mental calculation strategies (+ and –)

Activity sheet questions

- Use knowledge that addition can be done in any order to do mental calculations more efficiently. For example:
  - put the larger number first and count on
  - add three or four small numbers by putting the largest number first and/or by finding pairs totalling 9, 10 or 11

Written

1–2
- partition into '5 and a bit' when adding 6, 7, 8 or 9 (e.g. 47 + 8 = 45 + 2 + 5 + 3 = 50 + 5 = 55)

3
- partition into tens and units, then recombine (e.g. 34 + 53 = 30 + 50 + 4 + 3).

4
- **Find a small difference by counting up from the smaller to the larger number (e.g. 102 – 97).**

5–8
- **Identify near doubles, using doubles already known (e.g. 80 + 81).**
- Add and subtract mentally a 'near multiple of 10' to or from a two-digit number ... by adding or subtracting 10, 20, 30 ... and adjusting.
- Use patterns of similar calculations.
- Say or write a subtraction statement corresponding to a given addition statement, and vice versa.
- Use known number facts and place value to add/subtract mentally.
- Bridge through a multiple of 10, then adjust.

Teacher note

- The use of empty number lines to demonstrate small differences is useful, e.g. from 96 to 101, with arcs to indicate the jump from 96 to 100 and then on to 101.

i.e.

96   4   100   101   1

Answers

1   a. 25 + 16 =   **41**

    b. 29 + 18 =   **47**

2   a. 45 + 19 =   **64**

    b. 54 + 17 =   **71**

3   16 + 21 can be done like this. (10 + 6) + (20 +1) = 30 + 7 = 37

Do these in the same way.

    a. 25 + 43 =   **(20 + 5) + (40 + 3) = 60 + 8 = 68**

    b. 37 + 28 =   **(30 + 7) + (20 + 8) = 50 + 15 = 65**

    c. 46 + 57 =   **(40 + 6) + (50 + 7) = 90 + 13 = 103**

4   Do these by counting up.

    a. 103 – 98 =   **5**   c. 304 – 295 =   **9**

    b. 107 – 96 =   **11**   d. 502 – 494 =   **8**

5   a. 25 + 26 =   **51**

    b. How did you do it?   **e.g. I added 25 and 25 and 1.**

6   a. 33 + 32 =   **65**

    b. How did you do it?   **e.g. Double 32 + 1.**

7   a. 50 + 60 =   **110**

    b. How did you do it?   **e.g. I doubled 50 and added 10.**

8   a. 70 + 80 =   **150**

    b. How did you do it?   **e.g. Double 70 add 10.**

Name: _____   Date: _____

1   a. 25 + 16 = [____]

b. 29 + 18 = [____]

2   a. 45 + 19 = [____]

b. 54 + 17 = [____]

3   16 + 21 can be done like this. (10 + 6) + (20 +1) = 30 + 7 = 37

Do these in the same way.

a. 25 + 43 = [____]

b. 37 + 28 = [____]

c. 46 + 57 = [____]

4   Do these by counting up.

a. 103 – 98 = [____]

b. 107 – 96 = [____]

c. 304 – 295 = [____]

d. 502 – 494 = [____]

5   a. 25 + 26 = [____]

b. How did you do it? [____]

6   a. 33 + 32 = [____]

b. How did you do it? [____]

7   a. 50 + 60 = [____]

b. How did you do it? [____]

8   a. 70 + 80 = [____]

b. How did you do it? [____]

© Folens (copiable page)

Activity sheet questions

- Use knowledge that addition can be done in any order to do mental calculations more efficiently. For example:
  - put the larger number first and count on
  - add three or four small numbers by putting the largest number first and/or by finding pairs totalling 9, 10 or 11
  - partition into '5 and a bit' when adding 6, 7, 8 or 9 (e.g. 47 + 8 = 45 + 2 + 5 + 3 = 50 + 5 = 55)
  - partition into tens and units, then recombine (e.g. 34 + 53 = 30 + 50 + 4 + 3).
- Find a small difference by counting up from the smaller to the larger number (e.g. 102 – 97).
- Identify near doubles, using doubles already known (e.g. 80 + 81).

Written

1–6
- **Add and subtract mentally a 'near multiple of 10' to or from a two-digit number … by adding or subtracting 10, 20, 30 … and adjusting.**

7
- **Use patterns of similar calculations.**
- Say or write a subtraction statement corresponding to a given addition statement, and vice versa.
- Use known number facts and place value to add/subtract mentally.
- Bridge through a multiple of 10, then adjust.

Teacher note

- Children should be encouraged to use a wide range of mental calculation strategies and to verbalise the method chosen for each calculation. They should also have experience of recording such calculation strategies using informal jottings.

Answers

1. a. 26 + 11 = **37**   b. 38 – 11 = **27**

2. a. 163 + 11 = **174**   b. 279 – 11 = **268**

3. a. 54 + 9 = **63**   b. 62 – 9 = **53**

4. a. 193 + 9 = **202**   b. 458 – 9= **449**

5. a. 46 + 21 = **67**   b. 68 – 21 = **47**

6. a. 38 + 29 = **67**   b. 67 – 29 = **38**

7. Continue these patterns.

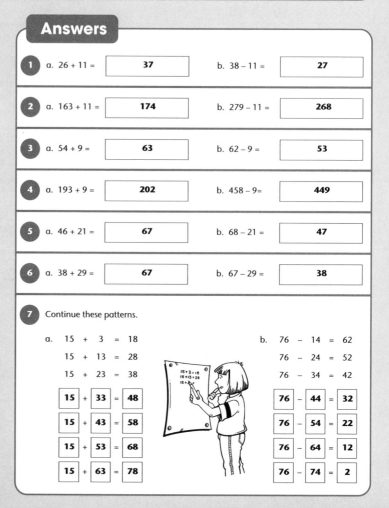

a.   15 + 3 = 18
     15 + 13 = 28
     15 + 23 = 38
     15 + **33** = **48**
     15 + **43** = **58**
     15 + **53** = **68**
     15 + **63** = **78**

b.   76 – 14 = 62
     76 – 24 = 52
     76 – 34 = 42
     76 – **44** = **32**
     76 – **54** = **22**
     76 – **64** = **12**
     76 – **74** = **2**

Name: _____ Date: _____

Mental calculation strategies (+ and –)

1 a. 26 + 11 = [   ]   b. 38 – 11 = [   ]

2 a. 163 + 11 = [   ]   b. 279 – 11 = [   ]

3 a. 54 + 9 = [   ]   b. 62 – 9 = [   ]

4 a. 193 + 9 = [   ]   b. 458 – 9= [   ]

5 a. 46 + 21 = [   ]   b. 68 – 21 = [   ]

6 a. 38 + 29 = [   ]   b. 67 – 29 = [   ]

7 Continue these patterns.

a. 15 + 3 = 18   b. 76 – 14 = 62

15 + 13 = 28   76 – 24 = 52

15 + 23 = 38   76 – 34 = 42

[   ] + [   ] = [   ]   [   ] – [   ] = [   ]

[   ] + [   ] = [   ]   [   ] – [   ] = [   ]

[   ] + [   ] = [   ]   [   ] – [   ] = [   ]

[   ] + [   ] = [   ]   [   ] – [   ] = [   ]

Activity sheet questions

- Use knowledge that addition can be done in any order to do mental calculations more efficiently. For example:
  - put the larger number first and count on
  - add three or four small numbers by putting the largest number first and/or by finding pairs totalling 9, 10 or 11
  - partition into '5 and a bit' when adding 6, 7, 8 or 9 (e.g. 47 + 8 = 45 + 2 + 5 + 3 = 50 + 5 = 55)
  - partition into tens and units, then recombine (e.g. 34 + 53 = 30 + 50 + 4 + 3).
- Find a small difference by counting up from the smaller to the larger number (e.g. 102 – 97).
- Identify near doubles, using doubles already known (e.g. 80 + 81).
- Add and subtract mentally a 'near multiple of 10' to or from a two-digit number … by adding or subtracting 10, 20, 30 … and adjusting.
- Use patterns of similar calculations.
- Use known number facts and place value to add/subtract mentally.

Written

1–4 ● **Say or write a subtraction statement corresponding to a given addition statement, and vice versa.**

5–7 ● **Bridge through a multiple of 10, then adjust.**

Teacher note

- Children should be encouraged to use a wide range of mental calculation strategies and to verbalise the method chosen for each calculation. They should also have experience of recording such calculation strategies using informal jottings.

Answers

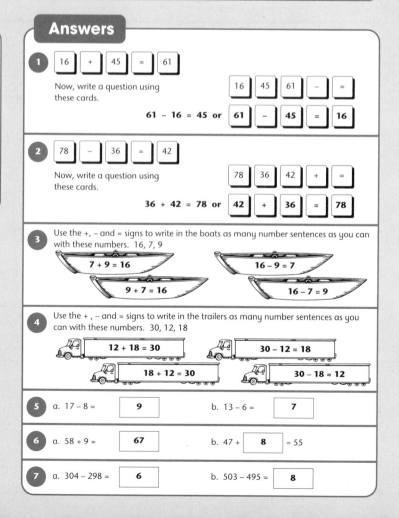

1. 16 + 45 = 61

   Now, write a question using these cards.

   16 45 61 – =

   61 – 16 = 45 or 61 – 45 = 16

2. 78 – 36 = 42

   Now, write a question using these cards.

   78 36 42 + =

   36 + 42 = 78 or 42 + 36 = 78

3. Use the +, – and = signs to write in the boats as many number sentences as you can with these numbers. 16, 7, 9

   7 + 9 = 16   **16 – 9 = 7**

   9 + 7 = 16   **16 – 7 = 9**

4. Use the + , – and = signs to write in the trailers as many number sentences as you can with these numbers. 30, 12, 18

   12 + 18 = 30   **30 – 12 = 18**

   18 + 12 = 30   **30 – 18 = 12**

5. a. 17 – 8 = **9**   b. 13 – 6 = **7**

6. a. 58 + 9 = **67**   b. 47 + **8** = 55

7. a. 304 – 298 = **6**   b. 503 – 495 = **8**

Name: _____   Date: _____

1 | 16 | + | 45 | = | 61 |

Now, write a question using these cards.

2 | 78 | – | 36 | = | 42 |

Now, write a question using these cards.

3 Use the +, – and = signs to write in the boats as many number sentences as you can with these numbers. 16, 7, 9

4 Use the + , – and = signs to write in the trailers as many number sentences as you can with these numbers. 30, 12, 18

5 a. 17 – 8 = [ ]   b. 13 – 6 = [ ]

6 a. 58 + 9 = [ ]   b. 47 + [ ] = 55

7 a. 304 – 298 = [ ]   b. 503 – 495 = [ ]

Activity sheet questions

Written

1–4   ● Use informal pencil and paper methods to support, record or explain HTU + TU, HTU + HTU.

5–6   Begin to use column addition for HTU + TU where the calculation cannot easily be done mentally.

Teacher note

● All written methods of calculation should be based initially on a firm foundation of mental methods and a solid understanding of the operations of addition and subtraction. Children should have developed an understanding of the role of each operation and the relationships between them, i.e. that addition and subtraction are inverses. Children should be encouraged to approximate at all times before calculating, using a mental method, in order to check whether an answer is sensible.

Answers

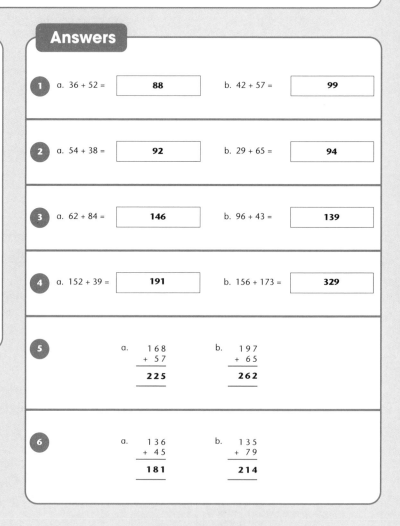

1   a. 36 + 52 =   **88**   b. 42 + 57 =   **99**

2   a. 54 + 38 =   **92**   b. 29 + 65 =   **94**

3   a. 62 + 84 =   **146**   b. 96 + 43 =   **139**

4   a. 152 + 39 =   **191**   b. 156 + 173 =   **329**

5   a.   168
        + 57
        225
    b.   197
        + 65
        262

6   a.   136
        + 45
        181
    b.   135
        + 79
        214

Name: _____ Date: _____

Pencil and paper procedures (+)

1 a. 36 + 52 = [ ]   b. 42 + 57 = [ ]

2 a. 54 + 38 = [ ]   b. 29 + 65 = [ ]

3 a. 62 + 84 = [ ]   b. 96 + 43 = [ ]

4 a. 152 + 39 = [ ]   b. 156 + 173 = [ ]

5

a.
```
  1 6 8
+   5 7
───────

───────
```

b.
```
  1 9 7
+   6 5
───────

───────
```

6

a.
```
  1 3 6
+   4 5
───────

───────
```

b.
```
  1 3 5
+   7 9
───────

───────
```

Activity sheet questions

Written

1–4 ● Use informal pencil and paper methods to support, record or explain HTU – TU, HTU – HTU.

5–6 Begin to use column subtraction for HTU – TU where the calculation cannot easily be done mentally.

Teacher note

● All written methods of calculation should be based initially on a firm foundation of mental methods and a solid understanding of the operations of addition and subtraction. Children should have developed an understanding of the role of each operation and the relationships between them, i.e. that addition and subtraction are inverses. Children should be encouraged to approximate at all times before calculating, using a mental method, in order to check whether an answer is sensible.

Answers

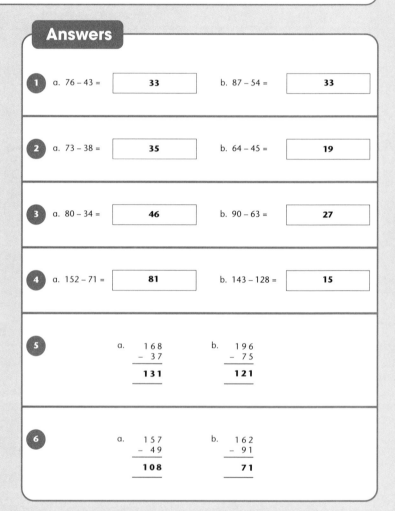

1 a. 76 – 43 = **33**   b. 87 – 54 = **33**

2 a. 73 – 38 = **35**   b. 64 – 45 = **19**

3 a. 80 – 34 = **46**   b. 90 – 63 = **27**

4 a. 152 – 71 = **81**   b. 143 – 128 = **15**

5
a.
```
  168
–  37
─────
  131
```
b.
```
  196
–  75
─────
  121
```

6
a.
```
  157
–  49
─────
  108
```
b.
```
  162
–  91
─────
   71
```

Name: _____ Date: _____

1 a. 76 – 43 = [　　　]   b. 87 – 54 = [　　　]

2 a. 73 – 38 = [　　　]   b. 64 – 45 = [　　　]

3 a. 80 – 34 = [　　　]   b. 90 – 63 = [　　　]

4 a. 152 – 71 = [　　　]   b. 143 – 128 = [　　　]

5
a.
```
  1 6 8
–   3 7
_____

_____
```
b.
```
  1 9 6
–   7 5
_____

_____
```

6
a.
```
  1 5 7
–   4 9
_____

_____
```
b.
```
  1 6 2
–   9 1
_____

_____
```

Understanding multiplication and division

Activity sheet questions

Oral
1–10
& Written
1

● Understand multiplication as repeated addition.
Read and begin to write the related vocabulary.

2–4

Extend understanding that multiplication can be done in any order.
● Understand division as grouping (repeated subtraction) or sharing.
Read and begin to write the related vocabulary.
Recognise that division is the inverse of multiplication, and that halving is the inverse of doubling.
● Begin to find remainders after simple division.
● Round up or down after division, depending on the context.

Teacher note

● Note the commutative law as it applies to multiplication, i.e. 5 x 3 and 3 x 5 give the same answer.

Oral questions

1. 3 times 5.
2. 4 twos are?
3. 8 multiplied by 2.
4. 6 tens are?
5. Multiply 5 by 8.
6. How many times bigger than 5 is 30?
7. What is the product of 3 and 2?
8. Double 10.
9. Is 25 a multiple of 2?
10. Is 40 a multiple of 5?

Answers

1. **15**		6. **6**	
2. **8**		7. **6**	
3. **16**		8. **20**	
4. **60**		9. **No**	
5. **40**		10. **Yes**	

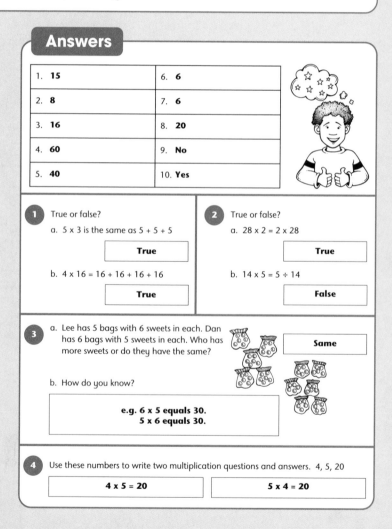

1 True or false?

a. 5 x 3 is the same as 5 + 5 + 5

> **True**

b. 4 x 16 = 16 + 16 + 16 + 16

> **True**

2 True or false?

a. 28 x 2 = 2 x 28

> **True**

b. 14 x 5 = 5 ÷ 14

> **False**

3 a. Lee has 5 bags with 6 sweets in each. Dan has 6 bags with 5 sweets in each. Who has more sweets or do they have the same?

> **Same**

b. How do you know?

> **e.g. 6 x 5 equals 30.**
> **5 x 6 equals 30.**

4 Use these numbers to write two multiplication questions and answers. 4, 5, 20

> **4 x 5 = 20**

> **5 x 4 = 20**

Name: _____ Date: _____

1.	6.
2.	7.
3.	8.
4.	9.
5.	10.

1 True or false?

a. 5 x 3 is the same as 5 + 5 + 5

[ ]

b. 4 x 16 = 16 + 16 + 16 + 16

[ ]

2 True or false?

a. 28 x 2 = 2 x 28

[ ]

b. 14 x 5 = 5 ÷ 14

[ ]

3 a. Lee has 5 bags with 6 sweets in each. Dan has 6 bags with 5 sweets in each. Who has more sweets or do they have the same?

[ ]

b. How do you know?

[ ]

4 Use these numbers to write two multiplication questions and answers. 4, 5, 20

[ ]   [ ]

Activity sheet questions

	○ Understand multiplication as repeated addition. Extend understanding that multiplication can be done in any order.
Oral 1–10 & Written 1–2	● Understand division as grouping (repeated subtraction) or sharing. Read and begin to write the related vocabulary.
3	Recognise that division is the inverse of multiplication, and that halving is the inverse of doubling.
4	● Begin to find remainders after simple division.
5	● Round up or down after division, depending on the context.

Teacher note

● Children need plenty of experience of situations in which a remainder is not appropriate and it is necessary to round up or down. For example, in the question: 'Egg boxes hold 6 eggs. How many would be needed to hold 40 eggs?', the answer is 7 rather than 6 rem. 4.

Oral questions

1. Share 16 between 2.
2. Share 30 between 5.
3. Divide 25 by 5.
4. How many fives make 35?
5. How many fours make 20?
6. What is half of 20?
7. Halve 40.
8. How many 10p pieces do you get for 60p?
9. How many 10p pieces do you get for 100p?
10. Is 55 a multiple of 5?

Answers

1. **8**		6. **10**	
2. **6**		7. **20**	
3. **5**		8. **6**	
4. **7**		9. **10**	
5. **5**		10. **Yes**	

1 True or false?

   a. 15 ÷ 3 is the same as 3 ÷ 15   **False**

   b. 55 ÷ 5 is the same as 5 ÷ 55   **False**

2   a. 16 ÷ 1 = **16**   b. 53 ÷ 1 = **53**

3 True or false?   a. 56 ÷ 7 = 8 and 7 x 8 = 56   **True**

                                  b. 72 ÷ 8 = 9 and 8 x 9 = 63   **False**

4 A grocer is putting 29 apples into boxes. Each box holds 4 apples.

   a. How many boxes can he fill?   **7**

   b. How many apples will be left over?   **1**

5 A supermarket is putting bread on its shelves. 10 loaves fill a shelf. There are 67 loaves. How many shelves will be needed?   **7**

Name: _____   Date: _____

1.	6.
2.	7.
3.	8.
4.	9.
5.	10.

1 True or false?

a. $15 \div 3$ is the same as $3 \div 15$

b. $55 \div 5$ is the same as $5 \div 55$

2 a. $16 \div 1 =$ _____   b. $53 \div 1 =$ _____

3 True or false?   a. $56 \div 7 = 8$ and $7 \times 8 = 56$

b. $72 \div 8 = 9$ and $8 \times 9 = 63$

4 A grocer is putting 29 apples into boxes. Each box holds 4 apples.

a. How many boxes can he fill?

b. How many apples will be left over?

apples

5 A supermarket is putting bread on its shelves. 10 loaves fill a shelf. There are 67 loaves. How many shelves will be needed?

© Folens (copiable page)

Activity sheet questions

Written

1–2
- To multiply by 10/100, shift the digits one/two places to the left.

3–4
- Use doubling or halving, starting from known facts (e.g. 8 x 4 is double 4 x 4).
- Say or write a division statement corresponding to a given multiplication statement.
- Use known number facts and place value to carry out mentally simple multiplications and divisions.

Teacher note

- Children should be encouraged to use a wide range of mental calculation strategies and to verbalise the method chosen for each calculation. They should also have experience of recording such calculation strategies using informal jottings.
- Children should not be encouraged to 'add a nought' in order to multiply by 10 as later in their maths they will discover this does not always work (e.g. decimal fractions).

Answers

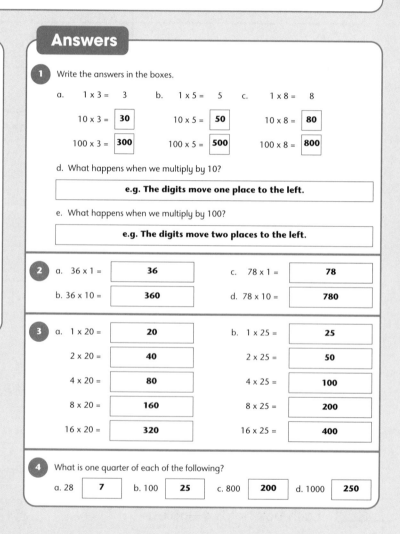

1. Write the answers in the boxes.

a.　1 x 3 = 　3　　　b.　1 x 5 = 　5　　c.　1 x 8 = 　8

　　10 x 3 = 　**30**　　　　10 x 5 = 　**50**　　　10 x 8 = 　**80**

　　100 x 3 = 　**300**　　　100 x 5 = 　**500**　　100 x 8 = 　**800**

d.　What happens when we multiply by 10?

e.g. The digits move one place to the left.

e.　What happens when we multiply by 100?

e.g. The digits move two places to the left.

2.　a.　36 x 1 = 　**36**　　　　c.　78 x 1 = 　**78**

　　b.　36 x 10 = 　**360**　　　d.　78 x 10 = 　**780**

3.　a.　1 x 20 = 　**20**　　　　b.　1 x 25 = 　**25**

　　　2 x 20 = 　**40**　　　　　2 x 25 = 　**50**

　　　4 x 20 = 　**80**　　　　　4 x 25 = 　**100**

　　　8 x 20 = 　**160**　　　　8 x 25 = 　**200**

　　　16 x 20 = 　**320**　　　16 x 25 = 　**400**

4.　What is one quarter of each of the following?

　a. 28　**7**　　b. 100　**25**　　c. 800　**200**　　d. 1000　**250**

Name: _____ Date: _____

1 Write the answers in the boxes.

a.　1 x 3 =　3　　　b.　1 x 5 =　5　　c.　1 x 8 =　8

　　10 x 3 = [ ]　　　　10 x 5 = [ ]　　　10 x 8 = [ ]

　　100 x 3 = [ ]　　　100 x 5 = [ ]　　100 x 8 = [ ]

d.　What happens when we multiply by 10?

[ ]

e.　What happens when we multiply by 100?

[ ]

2　a.　36 x 1 = [ ]　　　　　c.　78 x 1 = [ ]

　　b. 36 x 10 = [ ]　　　　　d.　78 x 10 = [ ]

3　a.　1 x 20 = [ ]　　　　　b.　1 x 25 = [ ]

　　2 x 20 = [ ]　　　　　　2 x 25 = [ ]

　　4 x 20 = [ ]　　　　　　4 x 25 = [ ]

　　8 x 20 = [ ]　　　　　　8 x 25 = [ ]

　　16 x 20 = [ ]　　　　　16 x 25 = [ ]

4 What is one quarter of each of the following?

a. 28 [ ]　　b. 100 [ ]　　c. 800 [ ]　　d. 1000 [ ]

Activity sheet questions

Oral
1–10
& Written
1–5

- To multiply by 10/100, shift the digits one/two places to the left.
- Use doubling or halving, starting from known facts (e.g. 8 x 4 is double 4 x 4).
- **Use known number facts and place value to carry out mentally simple multiplications and divisions.**

6
- Say or write a division statement corresponding to a given multiplication statement.

Teacher note

- Children should be encouraged to use a range of vocabulary for both multiplication and division, such as 'times', 'product', 'multiply', 'lots of', 'groups of', 'share', 'divide', etc.

Oral questions

1. 3 times 10.
2. Multiply 6 by 100.
3. 8 times what number gives 80?
4. What number multiplied by 100 gives 700?
5. Divide 600 by 10.
6. 900 divided by 100 equals?
7. Double 25.
8. What is half of 90?
9. Find one tenth of 50.
10. What is one hundredth of 800?

Answers

1.	**30**	6.	**9**
2.	**600**	7.	**50**
3.	**10**	8.	**45**
4.	**7**	9.	**5**
5.	**60**	10.	**8**

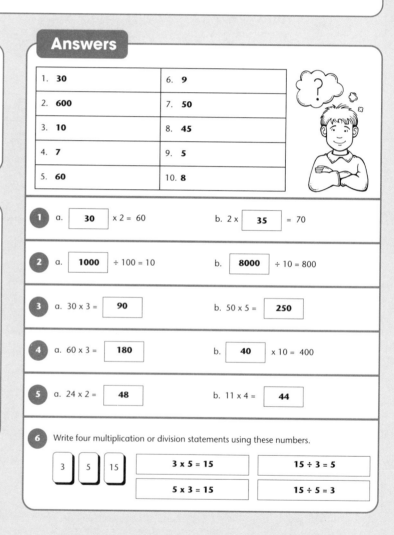

1 a. [**30**] x 2 = 60   b. 2 x [**35**] = 70

2 a. [**1000**] ÷ 100 = 10   b. [**8000**] ÷ 10 = 800

3 a. 30 x 3 = [**90**]   b. 50 x 5 = [**250**]

4 a. 60 x 3 = [**180**]   b. [**40**] x 10 = 400

5 a. 24 x 2 = [**48**]   b. 11 x 4 = [**44**]

6 Write four multiplication or division statements using these numbers.

[3] [5] [15]

3 x 5 = 15	**15 ÷ 3 = 5**
5 x 3 = 15	**15 ÷ 5 = 3**

Name: _____ Date: _____

1.	6.
2.	7.
3.	8.
4.	9.
5.	10.

1 a. [ ] x 2 = 60   b. 2 x [ ] = 70

2 a. [ ] ÷ 100 = 10   b. [ ] ÷ 10 = 800

3 a. 30 x 3 = [ ]   b. 50 x 5 = [ ]

4 a. 60 x 3 = [ ]   b. [ ] x 10 = 400

5 a. 24 x 2 = [ ]   b. 11 x 4 = [ ]

6 Write four multiplication or division statements using these numbers.

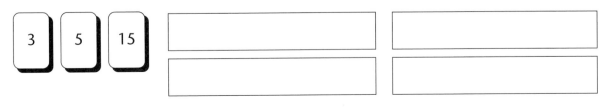

[3] [5] [15]

[ ]   [ ]

[ ]   [ ]

© Folens (copiable page)   MATHS WEEKLY ASSESSMENT: *Book 3*

Activity sheet questions

Written

1–6

- **Solve mathematical problems or puzzles, recognise simple patterns and relationships, generalise and predict. Suggest extensions by asking 'What if ...?'**
- Investigate a general statement about familiar numbers or shapes by finding examples that satisfy it.
- Explain methods and reasoning orally and, where appropriate, in writing.

Teacher note

- These questions emphasise the using and applying aspects of mathematics including trial and error, simplifying, being systematic, generalising, interpreting, etc. These are the abilities that allow children to make use of their mathematics in context. Many children who can successfully multiply, for example, have difficulty when faced with a multiplication question in problem form, often because of an inability to organise their thinking sufficiently. The abilities of simplifying, being systematic, etc. develop through repeated experiences of situations that require these skills.

Answers

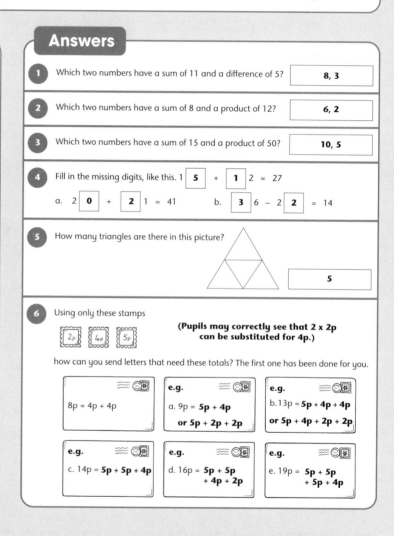

1. Which two numbers have a sum of 11 and a difference of 5? **8, 3**

2. Which two numbers have a sum of 8 and a product of 12? **6, 2**

3. Which two numbers have a sum of 15 and a product of 50? **10, 5**

4. Fill in the missing digits, like this. 1 **5** + **1** 2 = 27

   a. 2 **0** + **2** 1 = 41   b. **3** 6 – 2 **2** = 14

5. How many triangles are there in this picture? **5**

6. Using only these stamps

   2p 4p 5p

   (Pupils may correctly see that 2 x 2p can be substituted for 4p.)

   how can you send letters that need these totals? The first one has been done for you.

8p = 4p + 4p	e.g. a. 9p = **5p + 4p** or **5p + 2p + 2p**	e.g. b. 13p = **5p + 4p + 4p** or **5p + 4p + 2p + 2p**
e.g. c. 14p = **5p + 5p + 4p**	e.g. d. 16p = **5p + 5p + 4p + 2p**	e.g. e. 19p = **5p + 5p + 5p + 4p**

Name: _____   Date: _____

Reasoning about numbers or shapes

1 Which two numbers have a sum of 11 and a difference of 5?   [ ]

2 Which two numbers have a sum of 8 and a product of 12?   [ ]

3 Which two numbers have a sum of 15 and a product of 50?   [ ]

4 Fill in the missing digits, like this. 1 $\boxed{5}$ + $\boxed{1}$ 2 = 27

   a. 2 $\boxed{}$ + $\boxed{}$ 1 = 41   b. $\boxed{}$ 6 – 2 $\boxed{}$ = 14

5 How many triangles are there in this picture?

   [ ]

6 Using only these stamps

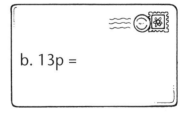

   how can you send letters that need these totals? The first one has been done for you.

   8p = 4p + 4p

   a. 9p =

   b. 13p =

   c. 14p =

   d. 16p =

   e. 19p =

Reasoning about numbers or shapes

Activity sheet questions

● Solve mathematical problems or puzzles, recognise simple patterns and relationships, generalise and predict. Suggest extensions by asking 'What if …?'

Written 1–6

● **Investigate a general statement about familiar numbers or shapes by finding examples that satisfy it.**

● **Explain methods and reasoning orally and, where appropriate, in writing.**

Teacher note

● Children need to appreciate that more than one example must be given to prove that a general statement is true.

Answers

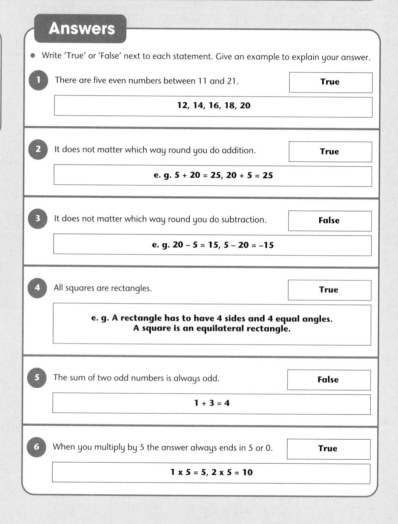

● Write 'True' or 'False' next to each statement. Give an example to explain your answer.

1 There are five even numbers between 11 and 21. **True**

12, 14, 16, 18, 20

2 It does not matter which way round you do addition. **True**

e. g. 5 + 20 = 25, 20 + 5 = 25

3 It does not matter which way round you do subtraction. **False**

e. g. 20 – 5 = 15, 5 – 20 = –15

4 All squares are rectangles. **True**

e. g. A rectangle has to have 4 sides and 4 equal angles.
A square is an equilateral rectangle.

5 The sum of two odd numbers is always odd. **False**

1 + 3 = 4

6 When you multiply by 5 the answer always ends in 5 or 0. **True**

1 x 5 = 5, 2 x 5 = 10

Name: _____   Date: _____

● Write 'True' or 'False' next to each statement. Give an example to explain your answer.

1 There are five even numbers between 11 and 21.

2 It does not matter which way round you do addition.

3 It does not matter which way round you do subtraction.

4 All squares are rectangles.

5 The sum of two odd numbers is always odd.

6 When you multiply by 5 the answer always ends in 5 or 0.

Problems involving 'real life'

Activity sheet questions

Written

1–8

- Solve word problems involving numbers in 'real life', using one or more steps, including finding totals.
  Explain how the problem was solved.
- Recognise all coins and notes. Understand and use £.p notation (for example, know that £3.06 is £3 and 6p).

Teacher note

- Children often find relatively simple calculations difficult when they are placed in a context. Such questions require the further ability of interpreting the question and extracting information.

Answers

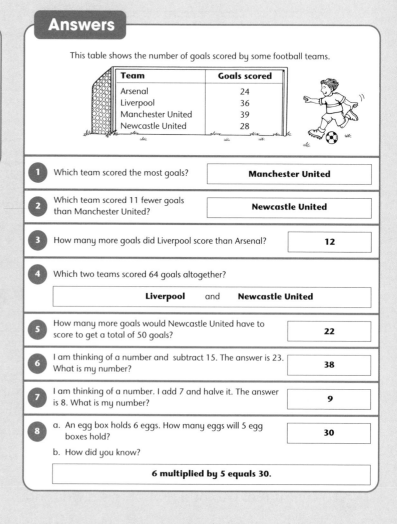

This table shows the number of goals scored by some football teams.

Team	Goals scored
Arsenal	24
Liverpool	36
Manchester United	39
Newcastle United	28

1 Which team scored the most goals?

Manchester United

2 Which team scored 11 fewer goals than Manchester United?

Newcastle United

3 How many more goals did Liverpool score than Arsenal?

12

4 Which two teams scored 64 goals altogether?

Liverpool and **Newcastle United**

5 How many more goals would Newcastle United have to score to get a total of 50 goals?

22

6 I am thinking of a number and subtract 15. The answer is 23. What is my number?

38

7 I am thinking of a number. I add 7 and halve it. The answer is 8. What is my number?

9

8 a. An egg box holds 6 eggs. How many eggs will 5 egg boxes hold?

30

b. How did you know?

6 multiplied by 5 equals 30.

Name: _____   Date: _____

Problems involving 'real life'

This table shows the number of goals scored by some football teams.

Team	Goals scored
Arsenal	24
Liverpool	36
Manchester United	39
Newcastle United	28

1 Which team scored the most goals?

2 Which team scored 11 fewer goals than Manchester United?

3 How many more goals did Liverpool score than Arsenal?

4 Which two teams scored 64 goals altogether?

_____ and _____

5 How many more goals would Newcastle United have to score to get a total of 50 goals?

6 I am thinking of a number and subtract 15. The answer is 23. What is my number?

7 I am thinking of a number. I add 7 and halve it. The answer is 8. What is my number?

8 a. An egg box holds 6 eggs. How many eggs will 5 egg boxes hold?

   b. How did you know?

Problems involving measures

Activity sheet questions

Written

1-6
- Solve word problems involving numbers in measures, using one or more steps, including finding totals.
  Explain how the problem was solved.
- Recognise all coins and notes. Understand and use £.p notation (for example, know that £3.06 is £3 and 6p).

Teacher note

- Maximise real-life measurement opportunities in the classroom, such as exploring the start and finish times of lessons and the duration of lunch, etc.

Answers

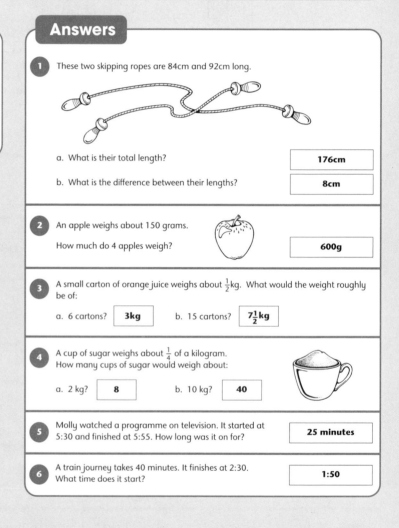

1 These two skipping ropes are 84cm and 92cm long.

  a. What is their total length? → **176cm**

  b. What is the difference between their lengths? → **8cm**

2 An apple weighs about 150 grams.
   How much do 4 apples weigh? → **600g**

3 A small carton of orange juice weighs about $\frac{1}{2}$kg. What would the weight roughly be of:

  a. 6 cartons? **3kg**   b. 15 cartons? **$7\frac{1}{2}$kg**

4 A cup of sugar weighs about $\frac{1}{4}$ of a kilogram.
   How many cups of sugar would weigh about:

  a. 2 kg? **8**   b. 10 kg? **40**

5 Molly watched a programme on television. It started at 5:30 and finished at 5:55. How long was it on for? → **25 minutes**

6 A train journey takes 40 minutes. It finishes at 2:30. What time does it start? → **1:50**

Name: _____ Date: _____

1 These two skipping ropes are 84cm and 92cm long.

a. What is their total length?

b. What is the difference between their lengths?

2 An apple weighs about 150 grams.

How much do 4 apples weigh?

3 A small carton of orange juice weighs about $\frac{1}{2}$kg. What would the weight roughly be of:

a. 6 cartons?

b. 15 cartons?

4 A cup of sugar weighs about $\frac{1}{4}$ of a kilogram.
How many cups of sugar would weigh about:

a. 2 kg?

b. 10 kg?

5 Molly watched a programme on television. It started at 5:30 and finished at 5:55. How long was it on for?

6 A train journey takes 40 minutes. It finishes at 2:30. What time does it start?

Activity sheet questions

Written

1-7
- Solve word problems involving numbers in 'real life', money and measures, using one or more steps, including finding totals and giving change, and working out which coins to pay.
Explain how the problem was solved.
- Recognise all coins and notes. Understand and use £.p notation (for example, know that £3.06 is £3 and 6p).

Teacher note

- Children often incorrectly write five pounds and eight pence as £5.8, £5.8p or £5.08p rather than £5.08 or 508p.

Answers

1 How many 10p coins could you swap for £1? | **10**

2 How many pence is: a. £8.75? | **875p** | b. £7.10? | **710p**

3 Write these prices in pounds and pence.

a. 529p | **£5.29** | b. 1007p | **£10.07**

4 Dinesh gets 60p a week in pocket money. How long is it before he can buy a new bag costing £3? | **5 weeks**

5 Jo has two £1 coins and one 50p coin. How much will she have left if she buys an ice cream for £1.20? | **£1.30**

6 a. How much would it cost to buy 1 box of breakfast flakes and 1 loaf of bread? | **£1.40**

b. How much change would there be from £2?

60p

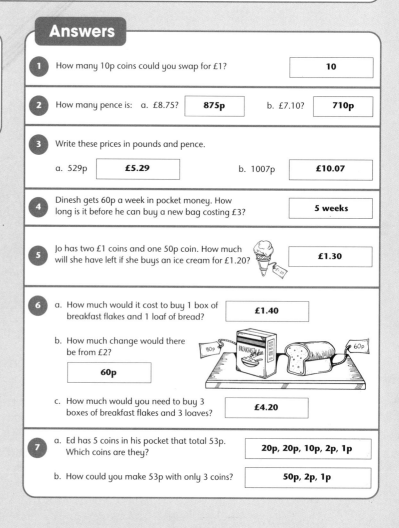

c. How much would you need to buy 3 boxes of breakfast flakes and 3 loaves? | **£4.20**

7 a. Ed has 5 coins in his pocket that total 53p. Which coins are they? | **20p, 20p, 10p, 2p, 1p**

b. How could you make 53p with only 3 coins? | **50p, 2p, 1p**

Name: _____   Date: _____

1 How many 10p coins could you swap for £1? [ ]

2 How many pence is: a. £8.75? [ ]   b. £7.10? [ ]

3 Write these prices in pounds and pence.

a. 529p [ ]   b. 1007p [ ]

4 Dinesh gets 60p a week in pocket money. How long is it before he can buy a new bag costing £3? [ ]

5 Jo has two £1 coins and one 50p coin. How much will she have left if she buys an ice cream for £1.20? [ ]

6 a. How much would it cost to buy 1 box of breakfast flakes and 1 loaf of bread? [ ]

b. How much change would there be from £2?

[ ]

c. How much would you need to buy 3 boxes of breakfast flakes and 3 loaves? [ ]

80p   BREAKFAST flakes   60p

7 a. Ed has 5 coins in his pocket that total 53p. Which coins are they? [ ]

b. How could you make 53p with only 3 coins? [ ]

Activity sheet questions

Written

1–4
- Solve a given problem by organising and interpreting numerical data in simple lists, tables and graphs, for example:
  - **Venn and Carroll diagrams (one criterion).**
  - simple frequency tables
  - pictograms – symbol representing two units
  - bar charts – intervals labelled in ones then twos.

Teacher note

- Experience of sorting with real objects is a very useful precursor to classifying with numbers. Sorting with Venn and Carroll diagrams at the same time and using the same items will help children to see how they relate to each other by highlighting their equivalent regions.

Answers

This Venn diagram shows some of the numbers between 1 and 20.

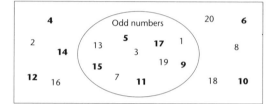

1 Add these numbers to the diagram. 5, 6, 10, 11, 15, 17 **(See above.)**

2 Add the number 14 to the diagram. Why does it go there?

> **e.g. 14 does not go in the ring because it is not odd.**

3 Finish the diagram so all the numbers between 1 and 20 are there. **(See above.)**

4 This Carroll diagram shows how Josh sorted some shapes.

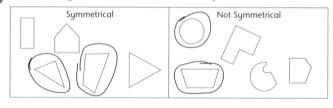

a. Draw rings around any shapes that are in the wrong place.

b. Draw a new shape on each side of the diagram.

Name: _____   Date: _____

Handling data

This Venn diagram shows some of the numbers between 1 and 20.

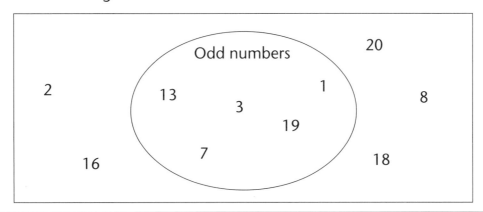

Odd numbers

2   13   3   1   20   8
19
16   7   18

1 Add these numbers to the diagram. 5, 6, 10, 11, 15, 17

2 Add the number 14 to the diagram. Why does it go there?

3 Finish the diagram so all the numbers between 1 and 20 are there.

4 This Carroll diagram shows how Josh sorted some shapes.

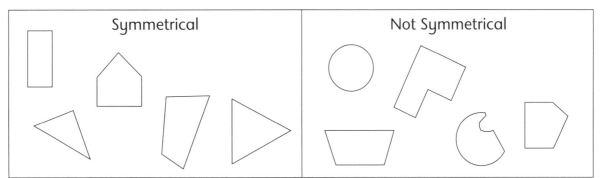

Symmetrical   Not Symmetrical

a. Draw rings around any shapes that are in the wrong place.

b. Draw a new shape on each side of the diagram.

Activity sheet questions

Written

1–6 ● Solve a given problem by organising and interpreting numerical data in simple lists, tables and graphs, for example:
- pictograms – symbol representing two units

7 - simple frequency tables
- bar charts – intervals labelled in ones then twos
- Venn and Carroll diagrams (one criterion).

Teacher note

● Some children will need plenty of opportunity to work with graphs on which one icon represents more than one item if they are to develop a real understanding of scale. The same graph can be reused by changing the scale. This helps to emphasise the need to understand the scale before the graph can be interpreted.

Answers

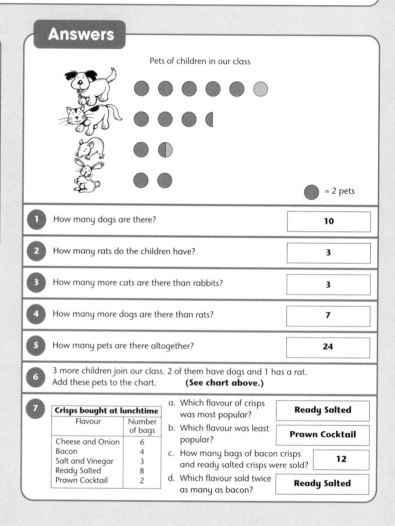

Pets of children in our class

◯ = 2 pets

1	How many dogs are there?	10
2	How many rats do the children have?	3
3	How many more cats are there than rabbits?	3
4	How many more dogs are there than rats?	7
5	How many pets are there altogether?	24
6	3 more children join our class. 2 of them have dogs and 1 has a rat. Add these pets to the chart. **(See chart above.)**	

7

Crisps bought at lunchtime	
Flavour	Number of bags
Cheese and Onion	6
Bacon	4
Salt and Vinegar	3
Ready Salted	8
Prawn Cocktail	2

a. Which flavour of crisps was most popular? **Ready Salted**

b. Which flavour was least popular? **Prawn Cocktail**

c. How many bags of bacon crisps and ready salted crisps were sold? **12**

d. Which flavour sold twice as many as bacon? **Ready Salted**

Name: _____ Date: _____

Pets of children in our class

= 2 pets

1 How many dogs are there?

2 How many rats do the children have?

3 How many more cats are there than rabbits?

4 How many more dogs are there than rats?

5 How many pets are there altogether?

6 3 more children join our class. 2 of them have dogs and 1 has a rat.
Add these pets to the chart.

7

Crisps bought at lunchtime	
Flavour	Number of bags
Cheese and Onion	6
Bacon	4
Salt and Vinegar	3
Ready Salted	8
Prawn Cocktail	2

a. Which flavour of crisps was most popular?

b. Which flavour was least popular?

c. How many bags of bacon crisps and ready salted crisps were sold?

d. Which flavour sold twice as many as bacon?

Handling data

Activity sheet questions

Written

1–8
- Solve a given problem by organising and interpreting numerical data in simple lists, tables and graphs, for example:
    - bar charts – intervals labelled in ones then twos
    - simple frequency tables
    - pictograms – symbol representing two units
    - Venn and Carroll diagrams (one criterion).

Teacher note

- Some children will need plenty of opportunity to work with charts where the numbers on the scales do not go up in ones. The same chart can be reused by changing the scale.

Answers

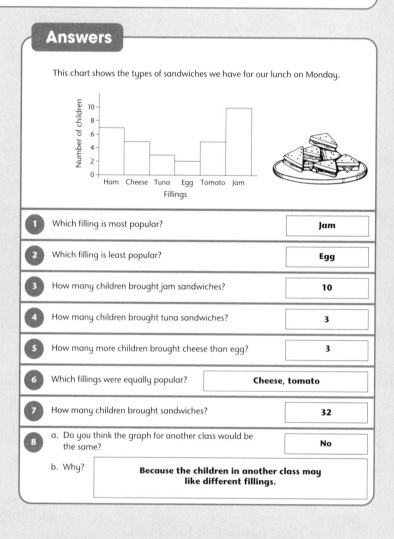

This chart shows the types of sandwiches we have for our lunch on Monday.

1	Which filling is most popular?	**Jam**
2	Which filling is least popular?	**Egg**
3	How many children brought jam sandwiches?	**10**
4	How many children brought tuna sandwiches?	**3**
5	How many more children brought cheese than egg?	**3**
6	Which fillings were equally popular?	**Cheese, tomato**
7	How many children brought sandwiches?	**32**
8	a. Do you think the graph for another class would be the same?	**No**
	b. Why?	**Because the children in another class may like different fillings.**

Name: _____   Date: _____

This chart shows the types of sandwiches we have for our lunch on Monday.

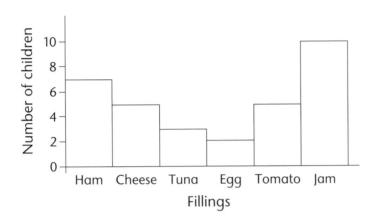

1	Which filling is most popular?	

2	Which filling is least popular?	

3	How many children brought jam sandwiches?	

4	How many children brought tuna sandwiches?	

5	How many more children brought cheese than egg?	

6	Which fillings were equally popular?	

7	How many children brought sandwiches?	

8 a. Do you think the graph for another class would be the same?

b. Why?

Measures

Activity sheet questions

Oral

1-10 ● Read and begin to write the vocabulary related to length, mass and capacity.

1-5   Know the relationships between kilometres and metres, metres and centimetres, kilograms and grams, litres and millilitres.

6-10 ● Suggest suitable units and measuring equipment to estimate or measure length, mass or capacity.

Written

1   Measure and compare using standard units (km, m, cm, kg, g, l, ml), including using a ruler to draw and measure lines to the nearest half centimetre.

2-3 ● Read scales to the nearest division (labelled or unlabelled).

    Record estimates and measurements to the nearest whole or half unit (e.g. 'about 3.5kg'), or in mixed units (e.g. '3m and 20cm').

    Begin to use decimal notation for metres and centimetres.

● Read and begin to write the vocabulary related to time.

    Use units of time and know the relationships between them (second, minute, hour, day, week, month, year).

    Suggest suitable units to estimate or measure time.

    Use a calendar.

    Read the time to 5 minutes on an analogue clock and a 12-hour digital clock, and use the notation 9:40.

Teacher note

● Children need to have practical experience of these units in order to understand them fully.

Oral questions

1. How many centimetres are in a metre?
2. True or false – 100 grams equals 1 kilogram?
3. How many millilitres are in a litre?
4. True or false – there are 1000 metres in a kilometre?
5. Write down 2 point 5 metres in another way.
6. Write something you might measure in centimetres.
7. Write something you might measure in kilograms.
8. What units would you measure the length of the playground in?
9. What units would you use to measure the width of your maths book?
10. What units would you use to measure how much a cup holds?

Answers

1.	**100**	6.	**e.g. The width of the table**
2.	**False**	7.	**e.g. My weight**
3.	**1000**	8.	**Metres**
4.	**True**	9.	**Centimetres**
5.	**Two and a half metres or Two metres and 50 centimetres**	10.	**Millilitres**

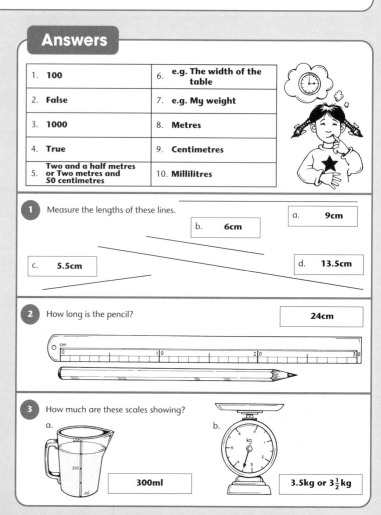

1 Measure the lengths of these lines.

a. **9cm**
b. **6cm**
c. **5.5cm**
d. **13.5cm**

2 How long is the pencil?   **24cm**

3 How much are these scales showing?

a. **300ml**   b. **3.5kg or $3\frac{1}{2}$kg**

Name: _____   Date: _____

1.	6.
2.	7.
3.	8.
4.	9.
5.	10.

1 Measure the lengths of these lines.

a.

b.

c.

d.

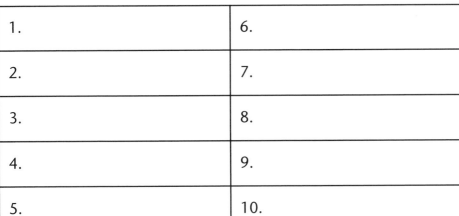

2 How long is the pencil?

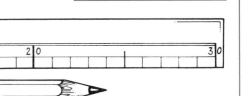

3 How much are these scales showing?

a.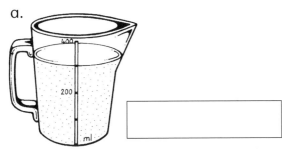

b.

Activity sheet questions

- Read and begin to write the vocabulary related to length, mass and capacity.
  Measure and compare using standard units (km, m, cm, kg, g, l, ml), including using a ruler to draw and measure lines to the nearest half centimetre.
  Know the relationships between kilometres and metres, metres and centimetres, kilograms and grams, litres and millilitres.
  Begin to use decimal notation for metres and centimetres.
- Suggest suitable units and measuring equipment to estimate or measure length, mass or capacity.
- Read scales to the nearest division (labelled or unlabelled).
  Record estimates and measurements to the nearest whole or half unit (e.g. 'about 3.5kg'), or in mixed units (e.g. '3m and 20cm').

Written 1–6

- **Read and begin to write the vocabulary related to time.**
  Use units of time and know the relationships between them (second, minute, hour, day, week, month, year).
  Suggest suitable units to estimate or measure time.
  Use a calendar.
  Read the time to 5 minutes on an analogue clock and a 12-hour digital clock, and use the notation 9:40.

Teacher note

- Children need experience in three aspects of time:
  1. **sequence** – becoming confident about the order in which time events take place
  2. **duration** – having a sense of the length of units of time
  3. **telling the time** – reading both digital and analogue clocks.
- Many children are able to 'read' digital time without having any real sense of what that time represents. This assessment focuses on the duration aspect of time.

Answers

1 Write the answers in the boxes. **(366 days in a leap year.)**
a. 1 year = **365** days b. 1 year = **52** weeks c. 1 year = **12** months

2 a. 1 week = **7** days c. 1 hour = **60** minutes
b. 1 day = **24** hours d. 1 minute = **60** seconds

3 Tick the correct answer.
I would measure the time until I go home in: **(Unless the test is given in the last hour before the children go home in which case the answer is 'minutes'.)**
weeks ☐ days ☐ hours ✓ minutes ☐ seconds ☐

4 Tick the correct answer.
I would measure the time taken to run across the playground in:
weeks ☐ days ☐ hours ☐ minutes ☐ seconds ✓

5 Write something that takes about: **(Answers are examples only.)**
a. 2 weeks **The Easter holidays**
b. 1 hour **The lunch break**
c. 5 minutes **Taking the register**
d. 10 seconds **Putting my watch on**

6 How long do you think: **(Answers are examples only.)**
a. you will have for maths today? **1 hour**
c. the summer holidays from school will be? **6 weeks**
b. you will be in bed tonight? **10 hours**
d. a football match lasts? **90 minutes ($1\frac{1}{2}$ hours)**

Name: _____ Date: _____

1 Write the answers in the boxes.

a. 1 year = [ ] days   b. 1 year = [ ] weeks   c. 1 year = [ ] months

2   a. 1 week = [ ] days   c. 1 hour = [ ] minutes

b. 1 day = [ ] hours   d. 1 minute = [ ] seconds

3 Tick the correct answer.
I would measure the time until I go home in:

weeks [ ]   days [ ]   hours [ ]   minutes [ ]   seconds [ ]

4 Tick the correct answer.
I would measure the time taken to run across the playground in:

weeks [ ]   days [ ]   hours [ ]   minutes [ ]   seconds [ ]

5 Write something that takes about:

a. 2 weeks [   ]

b. 1 hour [   ]

c. 5 minutes [   ]

d. 10 seconds [   ]

6 How long do you think:

a. you will have for maths today?   c. the summer holidays from school
will be?
[   ]   [   ]

b. you will be in bed tonight?   d. a football match lasts?
[   ]   [   ]

Measures

Activity sheet questions

- Read and begin to write the vocabulary related to length, mass and capacity.
  Measure and compare using standard units (km, m, cm, kg, g, l, ml), including using a ruler to draw and measure lines to the nearest half centimetre.
  Know the relationships between kilometres and metres, metres and centimetres, kilograms and grams, litres and millilitres.
  Begin to use decimal notation for metres and centimetres.
- Suggest suitable units and measuring equipment to estimate or measure length, mass or capacity.
- Read scales to the nearest division (labelled or unlabelled).
  Record estimates and measurements to the nearest whole or half unit (e.g. 'about 3.5kg'), or in mixed units (e.g. '3m and 20cm').
- Read and begin to write the vocabulary related to time.
  Use units of time and know the relationships between them (second, minute, hour, day, week, month, year).
  Suggest suitable units to estimate or measure time.

Written

1–3 Use a calendar.

4–5 Read the time to 5 minutes on an analogue clock and a 12-hour digital clock, and use the notation 9:40.

Teacher note

- Children need experience in using a variety of calendars as these can be arranged in different forms, e.g. weekly, monthly, yearly. Children need to record dates correctly, both in the extended and shortened versions, e.g. Saturday 5th February 2000 or 5.2.00. It is expected that children will know the months of the year in order and begin to spell them correctly.

Answers

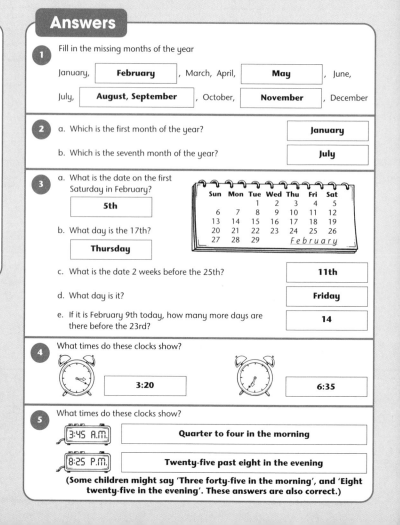

1 Fill in the missing months of the year

January, **February**, March, April, **May**, June, July, **August, September**, October, **November**, December

2
a. Which is the first month of the year? **January**
b. Which is the seventh month of the year? **July**

3
a. What is the date on the first Saturday in February? **5th**

	Sun	Mon	Tue	Wed	Thu	Fri	Sat
			1	2	3	4	5
	6	7	8	9	10	11	12
	13	14	15	16	17	18	19
	20	21	22	23	24	25	26
	27	28	29				*February*

b. What day is the 17th? **Thursday**

c. What is the date 2 weeks before the 25th? **11th**

d. What day is it? **Friday**

e. If it is February 9th today, how many more days are there before the 23rd? **14**

4 What times do these clocks show?

3:20   **6:35**

5 What times do these clocks show?

3:45 A.M. — **Quarter to four in the morning**

8:25 P.M. — **Twenty-five past eight in the evening**

(Some children might say 'Three forty-five in the morning', and 'Eight twenty-five in the evening'. These answers are also correct.)

Name: _____   Date: _____

30

---

1 Fill in the missing months of the year

January, [   ] , March, April, [   ] , June,

July, [,   ] , October, [   ] , December

---

2 a. Which is the first month of the year? [   ]

b. Which is the seventh month of the year? [   ]

---

3 a. What is the date on the first Saturday in February?

[   ]

	Sun	Mon	Tue	Wed	Thu	Fri	Sat
			1	2	3	4	5
	6	7	8	9	10	11	12
	13	14	15	16	17	18	19
	20	21	22	23	24	25	26
	27	28	29			*February*	

b. What day is the 17th?

[   ]

c. What is the date 2 weeks before the 25th?   [   ]

d. What day is it?   [   ]

e. If it is February 9th today, how many more days are there before the 23rd?   [   ]

---

4 What times do these clocks show?

[   ]   [   ]

---

5 What times do these clocks show?

`3:45 A.M.` [   ]

`8:25 P.M.` [   ]

Activity sheet questions

Written

1–2 ● Classify and describe 3D and 2D shapes, including the hemisphere, prism, semi-circle, quadrilateral … referring to properties such as reflective symmetry (2D), the number or shapes of faces, the number of sides/edges and vertices, whether sides/edges are the same length, whether or not angles are right angles … .

3 **Relate solid shapes to pictures of them.**

● Identify and sketch lines of symmetry in simple shapes, and recognise shapes with no lines of symmetry.
Sketch the reflection of a simple shape in a mirror line along one edge.

● Read and begin to write the vocabulary related to position, direction and movement: for example, describe and find the position of a square on a grid of squares with the rows and columns labelled.
Recognise and use the four compass directions N, S, E, W.

● Make and describe right-angled turns, including turns between the four compass points.
Identify right angles in 2D shapes and the environment.
Recognise that a straight line is equivalent to two right angles.
Compare angles with a right angle.

Teacher note

● Children need to appreciate that shapes can be in different orientations. They sometimes believe that triangles must have a horizontal base, for example. Children need access to solid shapes, without which they may think that a cube, for example, has only 9 edges because of how it appears in a 2D picture.

Answers

1 Describe these shapes. Use words like 'symmetry', 'sides', 'edges', 'faces' and 'vertices'.

a. A square — e.g. A square has 4 equal sides, 4 equal angles and 4 lines of symmetry.

b. A quadrilateral — e.g. A quadrilateral is any 2D shape that has 4 straight sides.

c. A hexagon — e.g. A hexagon is a 2D shape with 6 straight sides and 6 angles.

d. A hemisphere — e.g. A hemisphere is half a sphere with 1 flat circular face, 1 curved face and 1 edge, but 0 vertices.

e. A prism — e.g. A prism is a 3D shape that has the same cross-section all along its length.

For example, a triangular prism has 9 edges, 5 faces and 6 vertices.

2 Tick any statements that are true.

a. A square has no lines of symmetry. ☐

b. A hemisphere has 1 face that is a circle. ✓

c. A pentagon has 6 sides. ☐

d. The 2 end faces of a prism are the same. ✓

e. A rectangle always has 4 right angles. ✓

f. A triangle has 3 vertices. ✓

3 Name these shapes.

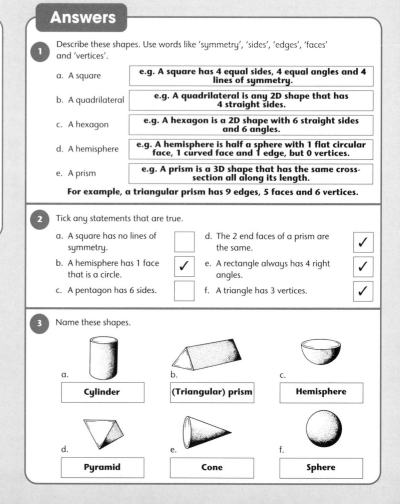

a. **Cylinder**

b. **(Triangular) prism**

c. **Hemisphere**

d. **Pyramid**

e. **Cone**

f. **Sphere**

Name: _____   Date: _____

1 Describe these shapes. Use words like 'symmetry', 'sides', 'edges', 'faces' and 'vertices'.

a. A square

b. A quadrilateral

c. A hexagon

d. A hemisphere

e. A prism

2 Tick any statements that are true.

a. A square has no lines of symmetry.

b. A hemisphere has 1 face that is a circle.

c. A pentagon has 6 sides.

d. The 2 end faces of a prism are the same.

e. A rectangle always has 4 right angles.

f. A triangle has 3 vertices.

3 Name these shapes.

a.

b.

c.

d.

e.

f.

Activity sheet questions

● Classify and describe 3D and 2D shapes, including the hemisphere, prism, semi-circle, quadrilateral … referring to properties such as reflective symmetry (2D), the number or shapes of faces, the number of sides/edges and vertices, whether sides/edges are the same length, whether or not angles are right angles … .
Relate solid shapes to pictures of them.

Written

1–2 ● **Identify and sketch lines of symmetry in simple shapes, and recognise shapes with no lines of symmetry.**

3 **Sketch the reflection of a simple shape in a mirror line along one edge.**

● Read and begin to write the vocabulary related to position, direction and movement: for example, describe and find the position of a square on a grid of squares with the rows and columns labelled.
Recognise and use the four compass directions N, S, E, W.

● Make and describe right-angled turns, including turns between the four compass points.
Identify right angles in 2D shapes and the environment.
Recognise that a straight line is equivalent to two right angles.
Compare angles with a right angle.

Teacher note

● provide mirrors and tracing paper to assist in checking for lines of symmetry.

Answers

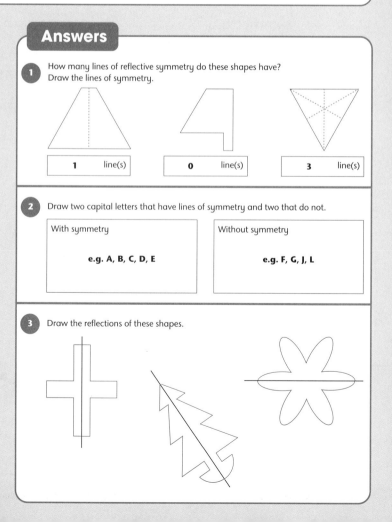

1 How many lines of reflective symmetry do these shapes have?
Draw the lines of symmetry.

| **1** line(s) | **0** line(s) | **3** line(s) |

2 Draw two capital letters that have lines of symmetry and two that do not.

With symmetry	Without symmetry
e.g. **A, B, C, D, E**	e.g. **F, G, J, L**

3 Draw the reflections of these shapes.

Name: _____ Date: _____

1 How many lines of reflective symmetry do these shapes have?
Draw the lines of symmetry.

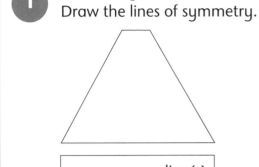

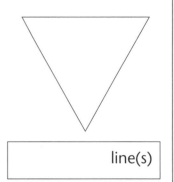

| line(s) | line(s) | line(s) |

2 Draw two capital letters that have lines of symmetry and two that do not.

With symmetry	Without symmetry

3 Draw the reflections of these shapes.

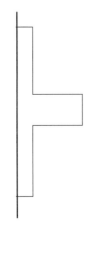
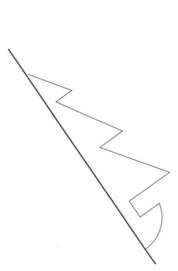

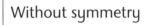

Activity sheet questions

- Classify and describe 3D and 2D shapes, including the hemisphere, prism, semi-circle, quadrilateral … referring to properties such as reflective symmetry (2D), the number or shapes of faces, the number of sides/edges and vertices, whether sides/edges are the same length, whether or not angles are right angles … .
- Relate solid shapes to pictures of them.
- Identify and sketch lines of symmetry in simple shapes, and recognise shapes with no lines of symmetry.
  Sketch the reflection of a simple shape in a mirror line along one edge.

Written

1   ● **Read and begin to write the vocabulary related to position, direction and movement: for example, describe and find the position of a square on a grid of squares with the rows and columns labelled.**

2–3   **Recognise and use the four compass directions N, S, E, W.**
- Make and describe right-angled turns, including turns between the four compass points.
  Identify right angles in 2D shapes and the environment.
  Recognise that a straight line is equivalent to two right angles.
  Compare angles with a right angle.

Teacher note

- Stress that the labels on the horizontal line should be given first, e.g. the letters in these cases.

Answers

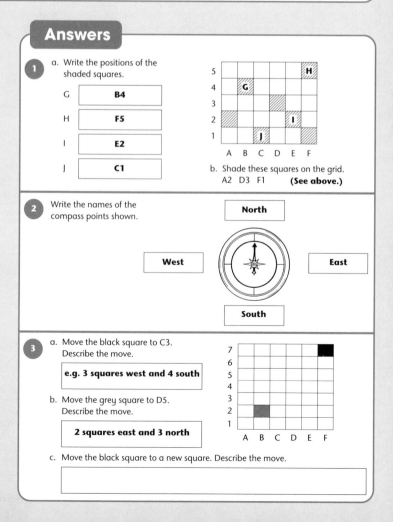

1 a. Write the positions of the shaded squares.

G   **B4**

H   **F5**

I   **E2**

J   **C1**

b. Shade these squares on the grid.
A2 D3 F1   **(See above.)**

2 Write the names of the compass points shown.

North

West   East

South

3 a. Move the black square to C3. Describe the move.

e.g. 3 squares west and 4 south

b. Move the grey square to D5. Describe the move.

2 squares east and 3 north

c. Move the black square to a new square. Describe the move.

Name: _____ Date: _____

1 a. Write the positions of the shaded squares.

G [ ]

H [ ]

I [ ]

J [ ]

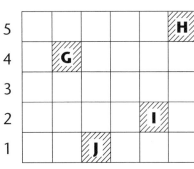

b. Shade these squares on the grid.
A2 D3 F1

2 Write the names of the compass points shown.

[ ]

[ ]      [ ]

[ ]

3 a. Move the black square to C3. Describe the move.

[ ]

b. Move the grey square to D5. Describe the move.

[ ]

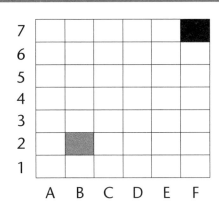

c. Move the black square to a new square. Describe the move.

[ ]

Shape and space

Activity sheet questions

- Classify and describe 3D and 2D shapes, including the hemisphere, prism, semi-circle, quadrilateral … referring to properties such as reflective symmetry (2D), the number or shapes of faces, the number of sides/edges and vertices, whether sides/edges are the same length, whether or not angles are right angles … .
Relate solid shapes to pictures of them.
- Identify and sketch lines of symmetry in simple shapes, and recognise shapes with no lines of symmetry.
Sketch the reflection of a simple shape in a mirror line along one edge.
- Read and begin to write the vocabulary related to position, direction and movement: for example, describe and find the position of a square on a grid of squares with the rows and columns labelled.
Recognise and use the four compass directions N, S, E, W.

Written

1–2
- **Make and describe right-angled turns, including turns between the four compass points.**
Recognise that a straight line is equivalent to two right angles.

3–5
Identify right angles in 2D shapes and the environment.
Compare angles with a right angle.

Teacher note

- Emphasise that a shape with a right angle does not necessarily have horizontal and vertical sides. The orientation of the shape does not affect the angle.

Answers

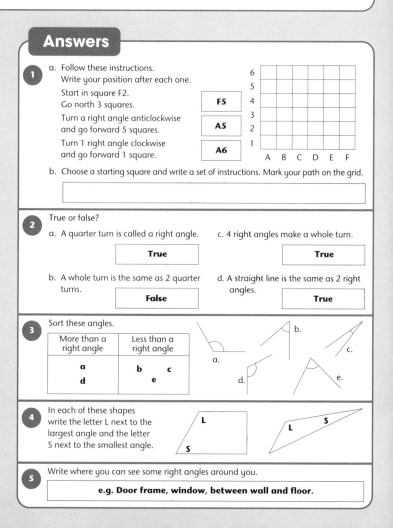

1 a. Follow these instructions.
Write your position after each one.

Start in square F2.
Go north 3 squares. — **F5**

Turn a right angle anticlockwise and go forward 5 squares. — **A5**

Turn 1 right angle clockwise and go forward 1 square. — **A6**

b. Choose a starting square and write a set of instructions. Mark your path on the grid.

2 True or false?

a. A quarter turn is called a right angle. **True**

c. 4 right angles make a whole turn. **True**

b. A whole turn is the same as 2 quarter turns. **False**

d. A straight line is the same as 2 right angles. **True**

3 Sort these angles.

More than a right angle	Less than a right angle
a	b c
d	e

4 In each of these shapes write the letter L next to the largest angle and the letter S next to the smallest angle.

5 Write where you can see some right angles around you.

e.g. Door frame, window, between wall and floor.

Name: _____   Date: _____

Shape and space

1 a. Follow these instructions.
Write your position after each one.

Start in square F2.
Go north 3 squares. ⬜

Turn a right angle anticlockwise
and go forward 5 squares. ⬜

Turn 1 right angle clockwise
and go forward 1 square. ⬜

6 | | | | | | |
5 | | | | | | |
4 | | | | | | |
3 | | | | | | |
2 | | | | | | |
1 | | | | | | |

A B C D E F

b. Choose a starting square and write a set of instructions. Mark your path on the grid.

_____

2 True or false?

a. A quarter turn is called a right angle.
⬜

c. 4 right angles make a whole turn.
⬜

b. A whole turn is the same as 2 quarter
turns.
⬜

d. A straight line is the same as 2 right
angles.
⬜

3 Sort these angles.

More than a right angle	Less than a right angle

a.
b.
c.
d.
e.

4 In each of these shapes
write the letter L next to the
largest angle and the letter
S next to the smallest angle.

5 Write where you can see some right angles around you.

_____

Record sheet

Number of answers

Names	Assessment No. 1	2	3	4	5	6	7	8	9	10	11	12	13	14	15	16	17	18	19	20	21	22	23	24	25	26	27	28	29	30	31	32	33	34